NETWORKS

ACROSS THE WATER

John McInnes, *Senior Author*

John Ryckman

Clayton Graves

NELSON CANADA

© Nelson Canada,
A Division of International Thomson Limited, 1985

All rights in this book are reserved

Published in 1985 by
Nelson Canada,
A Division of International Thomson Limited
1120 Birchmount Road
Scarborough, Ontario
M1K 5G4

ISBN 0-17-602348-8

Canadian Cataloguing in Publication Data

McInnes, John, 1927-
    Across the Water

(Networks)

ISBN 0-17-602348-8

I.   Readers (Elementary).   I. Ryckman, John, 1928-
II. Graves, Clayton.   III. Title.   IV. Series:
Networks (Toronto, Ont.)

PE1119.M252 1985   428.6   C85-098608-7

Printed and bound in Canada

Contents

Welcome

Welcome, children.
I'm happy you're here.
We're all going to have
A wonderful year.

We'll read
And we'll write
And we'll sing
And we'll play.

We'll build
And we'll paint
And learn new things
Each day.

In School Today

In school today,
my teacher said,
"Welcome, Brad.
I like your big brown eyes."

I think my teacher likes me.

In school today,
my teacher said,
"Welcome, Maria.
I like your curly hair."

I think my teacher likes me.

In school today,
my teacher said,
"Welcome, Josh.
I like your happy smile."

I think my teacher likes me.

In school today,
our teacher said,
"Welcome, everyone.
I'm happy to see you."

We think our teacher likes us.

Where's Charlie?

A Surprise

Who Likes to Read?

"Who-oo-oo likes to read?"

"I like to read,"
said the frog.
"I like to read songs."

"Who-oo-oo likes to read?"

"I like to read,"
said the beaver.
"I like to read blueprints."

"Who-oo-oo likes to read?"

"I like to read,"
said the goose.
"I like to read maps."

"Who-oo-oo likes to read?"

"I like to read,"
said the raccoon.
"I like to read cookbooks."

"Who-oo-oo likes to read?"

"I like to read,"
said the rabbit.
"I like to read weather reports."

"Who-oo-oo likes to read?"

"We like to read,"
said all the animals.

"That's who-oo-oo!"

I Wonder

I see some words.

I wonder what they say.

I see some words.

I wonder what they say.

I see some words.

I wonder what they say.

I see a chart.

I wonder what it says.

I see some signs.

I wonder what they say.

I see a note
from the teacher.

I *know* what it says!
Do you?

Something Happened on the Way

I started out for school today,
and something happened
on the way.

My cat followed me.

So then...
I had to go back home again.

I started out for school today,
and something happened
on the way.

A truck splashed me.

So then...
I had to go back home again.

I started out for school today,
and something happened
on the way.

A dog took my lunch.

So then...
I had to go back home again.

I started out for school today,
and something happened
on the way.

I lost my note.

So then...
I had to go back home again.

I started out for school today.
Nothing happened
on the way.

So...here I am!

Five Silly Billy Goats

Five silly billy goats
Fishing by the shore
Tried to catch an octopus.
Then there were four.

Four silly billy goats
Climbing up to see
What was in the eagle's nest.
Then there were three.

Three silly billy goats
Visiting the zoo
Went to feed the grizzly bear.
Then there were two.

42

Two silly billy goats
Sleeping in the sun
Didn't see the crocodile.
Then there was one.

One silly billy goat
Looking for some fun
Bumped into a buffalo.
Then there were none.

44

Five silly billy goats
Home safe and sound.
Each one learned a lesson:
DON'T FOOL AROUND!

45

Small Mysteries

On my way to school today,
I saw a kite in a tree.

I wonder how it got there.

On my way to school today,
I saw two flags on a roof.

I wonder how they got there.

On my way to school today,
I saw three trees on a truck.

I wonder how they got there.

On my way to school today,
I saw four pumpkins on a doorstep.

I wonder how they got there.

On my way to school today,
I saw five signs on the street.

I wonder how they got there.

On my way to school today,
I saw one roller skate,
two elephants,
three cuckoo clocks,
four picture frames,
five broken chairs,
and ME
in a garage sale.

I know how I got there!

Wet Is ...

Wet is...

soap suds foaming in the sink,
soap bubbles bursting on your nose,
a bar of soap shooting from your hands,
and a teddy bear
you're not supposed to wash.

Wet is...

warm mud squishing through your toes,
sticky mud clinging to your hands,
mushy mud patted into pies,
and mud fights
you're not supposed to have.

Wet is. . .
still water shining in the sun,
your own face looking back at you,
a new cap floating out of reach,
and a slippery log
you're not supposed to stand on.

Wet is…
snowflakes falling on your nose,
snowmen growing in your garden,
snowballs melting in your boots,
and a kitchen floor
you're not supposed to walk on.

How Do You Get Across the Water?

One morning
Dragon went for a walk.
He came to the water
and stopped.
Along came Beaver.

"How do you get
across the water?"
asked Dragon.

"I swim," said Beaver.
"Follow me."

"Not I," said Dragon.
"I don't want to get
my tail wet."

Along came Duck.

"How do you get
across the water?"
asked Dragon.

"I paddle," said Duck.
"Follow me."

"Not I," said Dragon.
"I don't want to get
my tail wet."

Along came Frog.

"How do you get
across the water?"
asked Dragon.

"I hop," said Frog.
"Follow me."

"Not I," said Dragon.
"I don't want to get
my tail wet."

Along came Crane.

"How do you get
across the water?"
asked Dragon.

"I wade," said Crane.
"Follow me."

"Not I," said Dragon.
"I don't want to get
my tail wet."

Along came Ant.

"How do you get
across the water?"
asked Dragon.

"I sail on a leaf," said Ant.
"Follow me."

"Not I," said Dragon.
"I don't want to get
    my tail wet."

Along came Raccoon.

"How do you get
across the water?"
asked Dragon.

"I run across a log," said Raccoon.
"And I don't get my tail wet.
Follow me."

And that's just what Dragon did.

Row, Row, Row Your Boat

Traditional

Row, row,
Row your boat
Gently down the stream.
Merrily, merrily,
Merrily, merrily,
Life is but a dream.

What a Dirty Kitten!

What a dirty kitten!

What a dirty bird!

What a dirty floor!

What a dirty window!

What a dirty street!

What a dirty me!

After a Bath

by Aileen Fisher

After a bath
I try, try, try
to wipe myself
till I'm dry, dry, dry.

Hands to wipe
and fingers and toes
and two wet legs
and a shiny nose.

Just think how much
less time I'd take
if I were a dog
and could shake, shake, shake.

Rainy Day

One rainy day, Dragon said,
"Mother, may I go out
to play?"

Mother Dragon said,
"Not just now.
It's raining."

Dragon said,
"Mother, now may I go out
to play?"

Mother Dragon said,
"Not just now.
It's raining."

Dragon said,
"Mother, NOW may I go out
to play?"

Mother Dragon said,
"Not just now.
It's raining."

Dragon said,
"Mother, **NOW** may I go out
to play?"

Mother Dragon said,
"Not just now.
It's raining."

Dragon said,
"Mother, **NOW** may I go out
to play?"

"Yes," said Mother Dragon.
"**NOW** you may go out
   to play."

"MOTHER!..."

Good Morning When It's Morning

by Mary Ann Hoberman

Good morning when it's morning
Good night when it is night,
Good evening when it's dark out
Good day when it is light,
Good morning to the sunshine
Good evening to the sky,
And when it's time to go away,
Goodbye,
Goodbye,
Goodbye.

Senior Editor: Deborah Gordon Lewi
Editor: Jocelyn Van Huyse
Design and Art Direction: Rob McPhail
Cover Design: Taylor/Levkoe Associates Limited
Cover Illustration: Brenda Clark
Typesetting: Trigraph Inc.
Film: Herzig Somerville Limited
Printing: M M & T

Acknowledgements

All selections in this book have been written or adapted by John McInnes, John Ryckman, and Clayton Graves, with the exception of the following:

After a Bath by Aileen Fisher: Reprinted by permission of the author, Aileen Fisher. Copyright © 1981.

Good Morning When It's Morning by Mary Ann Hoberman: Reprinted by permission of Russell and Volkening, Inc., as agents for the author. Copyright © 1974 by Mary Ann Hoberman.

Illustrations

Brenda Clark: 56-68, 69; Marie-Louise Cusack: 29-34; Jenny Duda: 17-22, 46-51; Eugenie Fernandes: 52-55; Rowesa Gordon: 94-95; Linda Hendry: 82; Barbara Klunder: 10-16; Paul McCusker: 83-93; San Murata: 40-45; David Partington: 70-81; Lisa Smith: 23-28; Roslyn Schwartz: 35-39; Paula Van Rassel: 4-5

Photographs

Birgitte Nielsen: 6-9

1234567890 MMT 1098765